Light
From The
Birdcage

Stories from an abandoned
Great Lakes lighthouse

HURON
PHOTO.COM

∘ETAOIN PUBLISHING∘
www.etaoinpublishing.com

Publisher: Etaoin Publishing
             Saginaw, MI
             www.EtaoinPublishing.com

             Huron Photo
             Saginaw Michigan
             www.huronphoto.com

Paperback ISBN 978-1-955474-02-3
Hardcover ISBN 978-1-955474-04-7

Dedicated to the men and women
who have kept the light shining as a
becon of hope.

Introduction

This is a fictional story about a day at the abandoned Waugoshance lighthouse that is intertwined with facts and true tales of historic Great Lakes lighthouses. I have made every effort to provide accurate facts and information from resource books, websites and my visits to many lighthouses.

Growing up in Michigan and being fascinated by lighthouses and their stories, I have had a curiosity about these maritime aids to navigation for most of my life. I have visited many old historic lighthouses that stand along the shoreline of the Great Lakes. With many books that have already been published about them, I did not want to just write another book with a series of redundant facts about the historic beacons. I decided instead to tell the story of one of the oldest and most endangered lighthouses in the United States of America. Although I have never actually spent a night in the Waugoshance Lighthouse, I wanted to tell its story in a way that makes the reader feel as if they are immersed in the world of the old forgotten and decaying structure. The parts of this book describing the time living in isolation for a day at the lighthouse are fiction, but the information about Waugoshance along with the stories of dedicated and heroic keepers is factual.

Chapter 1

Isolation

I stood on the crumbling stone cribbing blocks of the abandoned Waugoshance Lighthouse as the *Ships Ahoy* slowly bobbed up and down in the waves of Lake Michigan and floated away from the enormous jagged broken stone slabs. Captain Bob stood near the aft end of the thirty foot boat as I tossed him the end of the rope I was holding while we loaded my backpack and other things onto what was left of the man-made structure. As he pulled in the rope and the boat drifted further away, he yelled at me, "See ya tomorrow about four!"

"I'll be here!" I told him with my right hand up to my mouth to project my voice. "It's not like I'm goinna go anywhere."

3

He gave a little chuckle, then turned around, walked over to the wheel and grabbed it with his left hand. He reached over with his right hand and pushed down on the throttle. My ride sped off toward the horizon and eventually disappeared, leaving only a faint line in Lake Michigan where the water had been churned up by the engine's propeller. I thought the name of his boat was ridiculous, but I wanted him to pick me back up, so I was not going to make fun of it. I am sure I would not have been the first person to poke fun at a name that was chosen for its pun, but I did not want to take any chances.

Standing on what remained of the man-made island, and looking up at the bricks in the tower, I wondered if it would topple over on me, even though it has been standing for over a century and a half. I walked into the ruins of the Waugoshance Lighthouse, and my first thought was, It looks like a bomb went off in here. Unfortunately, that is what actually happened. It was not the work of a terrorist or an unfortunate accident; the United States had used it for target practice during World War II.

Several gulls and cormorants were circling overhead, looking down at me and wondering who had come into their man-made sanctuary. Bird feces streamed down from the top of the walls like a Jackson Pollock painting, and the vile aroma was the most putrid thing I had ever smelled. It reminded me of ammonia vapors, and I imagined what the porta potties smelled like at an asparagus festival.

The gray and white gulls looked less threatening than the cormorants. If you have never seen a cormorant, they are a bird about the size of a goose but are all black except for some orange skin on their head. They have a long snake-like neck and live on a diet of fish. They dive into the water to catch their prey and an adult cormorant can eat up to a pound of fish each day. In the past few decades, their population has grown extensively in the northern Great Lakes region. They are loathed by sport fishermen because of the great numbers of fish they eat. They nest on the lighthouses along the Straits of Mackinac, and their acid-like excrement is extremely destructive to the man-made structures. The organizations that have taken to preserving the old lighthouses have installed noise cannons to scare off the birds in the hope that they will stay away from the old historic structures.

5

Unfortunately, no attempt has been made to control the birds at Waugoshance.

I walked through the archway at the bottom of the tower away from the curious eyes of the birds flying overhead. The walls at the base of the tower were about five feet thick. The entrance was more like a short tunnel than a doorway. I was planning on climbing the cast iron spiral staircase to the lantern room, but I was surprised to find out that it had been replaced by a makeshift scaffolding.

Then I remembered reading somewhere that several years ago some enterprising and scrupulous thieves had stolen the staircase. The resourceful bandits probably did it during the winter when they could reach the lighthouse over the ice by snowmobile or a four wheel drive truck. I hope they used the old stairs in a house or something worthy of their historic significance. They had felt the footsteps of many keepers' shoes climbing up and down the tower over the years. Most likely they sold the old staircase for scrap, like some discarded, useless junk that no one wanted. As much as I wanted to see the view from the top of the tower, I decided to wait before I made the climb up the unstable and rickety scaffolding.

I had been on a personal quest to visit all the lighthouses in Michigan. I had visited most of the beacons on land in both the Upper and Lower Peninsulas, I had been working my way around the lakes, seeing lighthouses on islands and offshore cribs. I had contacted the people at the nonprofit group Save Waugoshance Lighthouse, and the president of the organization asked if I wanted to spend the night. He told me about the isolation challenges at the nearby White Shoal Lighthouse and wondered if I would be interested in living at Waugoshance for twenty-four hours. He probably thought I was crazy, or stupid, or both for accepting his offer, but I figured why not, so here I was.

I had brought my laptop so I could keep a journal of my experience. I doubted anyone would read it, but what else was I going to do, stuck on a man-made island in Lake Michigan? I was not sure how good of a read it would be anyway; my old high school English teacher Mrs. Campbell, always liked to tell me I was a poor student, and I struggled to get a C in her class. I hoped the battery in my computer would last for most of my stay. I liked to write on it because I am dyslexic and without it I had a terrible time spelling words and coming up with correct grammar. The autocorrect feature could be a pain in the butt sometimes, but without it, I found it nearly impossible for me to write anything coherent.

The accommodations were rather sparse after the fire gutted the old lighthouse. The only thing left of it was the stuff that would not burn, like the bricks and iron framework. I had brought along a lightweight camping chair along with a cot, a sleeping bag and some blankets for someplace comfortable to sleep. I had also packed a rechargeable LED lantern. I could either charge it with a small solar panel or a hand crank built into the side of the base. I wanted to have something to illuminate the top of the tower. A lighthouse without a light is like a corpse—just a body without any life or purpose.

Since I was staying for twenty-four hours, I had to bring along food to eat. I had a couple cases of water and a cooler with ice that had lunch meat and cheese for sandwiches. It also had some Faygo Redpop. I miss drinking the "good stuff" with real sugar, but I switched to diet after my heart attack and promised my doctor I would lose weight. I also had Spatz bread for my sandwiches. A bag of Cherry Republic spicy trail mix and some fudge I got in Mackinaw City.

Yeah, I know I said I was trying to drop a few pounds, but I figured I might as well get some fudge for a treat; besides, it had walnuts in it, and that's healthy, right? I also made sure to pick up a pasty in St. Ignace on the other side of the bridge. That would be the Mackinac Bridge if you are not familiar with the gap between Michigan's two peninsulas, but most Michiganians know what bridge you are talking about when you mention "the bridge".

Chapter 2

The First Crib
Lighthouse

Waugoshance Lighthosue has been reduced to three main structural components: stone, brick and iron. Everything else that could burn is gone. I guess you could also say bird poop now makes up a considerable portion of the lighthouse. It streaks down from the top of the walls and the square holes that once had glass windows before the storms shattered them into pieces. Now the gulls and other birds like to stand in the unrestricted openings. After pilots used the lighthouse for bombing practice while training for WWII, the bombs started a fire that turned everything combustible into ash. The wooden floor of the second story and the roof are gone. What remains of the keeper's quarters are just iron covered

10

walls that reach two stories high and then abruptly end.

The tower was once covered in iron sheeting, but that fell into Lake Michigan several years ago, and now the cream city bricks are exposed to the elements again. The yellow bricks were manufactured in Milwaukee and got their name because of the dairy industry that is prevalent in the Wisconsin area. Supposedly, that is where L. Frank Baum got the idea of the Yellow Brick Road for *The Wizard of Oz*. I think I am writing too much, but then again I don't have a volleyball with a bloody handprint to talk to like Tom Hanks in *Cast Away*.

The lighthouse was built in 1851 to mark the shallow shoals near the entrance of the Straits of Mackinac. A large wooden box called a crib was built on Helena Island fourteen miles to the north. It was about 50 feet square and then towed by a steamship across the straits to the Waugoshance shoal and sunk with rocks to build a foundation. Large slabs of…

I was in the middle of writing about the lighthouse when I heard a boat outside. I went out to see what it was, and I heard a loud gasp like a crowd watching a pitcher getting hit in the face with a line drive from a batter. They were passengers on a Shepler's boat on a lighthouse tour. The tourists were shocked to see someone at the abandoned lighthouse.

The captain slid his window open and shouted out to me. "You ok? Are you stranded?"

"Yeah, I'm fine. The *Ships Ahoy* dropped me off so I could spend the night."

"You did not make fun of Captain Bob's charter boat, did you? He hates that. He should change the name if it is going to get him riled up every time someone makes fun of it."

I laughed and yelled back, "No, I want to be picked up tomorrow! I have permission from the lighthouse society to do an isolation challenge."

"Ok! Stay safe. They say this old lighthouse is haunted." And with that, the blue and white passenger ferry left for the next lighthouse. A few of the passengers waved, but most of them were busy taking photos or trying to figure out how to work their phone to take a photo.

The lighthouse sits on large slabs of sandstone that weigh several tons each. It is hard to imagine what it took to put them in place in 1851; they did not have diesel-powered hydraulic cranes back then. For the most part, the workers had to set them with back-breaking work using ropes, timbers and pulleys. The crib that makes up the little man-made island used to be larger, but the ice has worn it down to just an oval shaped stone island sticking out of the water. It is not much larger than the lighthouse that stands on it. It has a small ledge around the outside with just enough room to walk around the perimeter of the poo covered iron walls.

I heard a lot of strange thumping and popping noises. The rusty brown boiler plate soaked up the heat from the sun like a black car sitting in a large empty parking lot. I thought it was the iron expanding and contracting in the Michigan summer sunshine. I could see how former keepers and people who have seen the decaying old lighthouse thought it was haunted.

Chapter 3

A Prankster Ghost

One story that began to circulate in the early 1900s was that Waugoshance's former keeper John Herman's spirit roamed the offshore beacon. Herman was the head keeper from 1890 to 1900. He was a prankster and enjoyed pulling practical jokes on his assistant keepers. Herman was also known to drink heavily.

One day after he had a little too much to drink, he thought it would be funny to lock the assistant keeper in the lantern room at the top of the tower. When the keeper was polishing the lamp, Herman quietly climbed the now missing spiral staircase. Upon reaching the top, he quickly closed the door to the lantern room and locked it. The assistant heard Herman laughing as he stumbled down the winding staircase. The assistant yelled out for

Herman to come back and release him from his high rise confinement, but he never answered his calls for help. Eventually, someone came and unlocked the door, but John Herman was nowhere to be found. They looked all over the isolated light station for him; they thought he may have passed out somewhere. The small wooden lighthouse boat was still sitting in its cradle, so he had not taken it into town. It was believed that in his drunken state, he staggered off the crib and fell into Lake Michigan.

The ghost story of the inebriated keeper was told for generations. It was several decades after the supposed incident had happened that John Herman's grave was discovered on Mackinac Island. The graveyard next to Saint Mary's Catholic Church was moved toward the center of the island to make room for more buildings downtown. It was in this cemetery that his headstone had been forgotten. I think that Herman's antics finally got him fired, and rather than living in disgrace, the story of him drowning sounded better than him being fired for being incompetent and drunk. The story of Keeper Herman haunting the lighthouse lives on as people continue to share it.

It is also believed that a worker died during the construction of the lighthouse in 1851. No record of his death exists, but with the manual labor that was needed to construct the tower and buildings, I would not be surprised if more than one death occurred.

Chapter 4

The Birdcage

I don't put a lot of stock in ghost stories, but I gotta say that the old lighthouse is spooky in a beautiful sort of way. It has what is known as a "bird cage" style lantern room at the top of the tower. The old, corroded iron bars once held glass windows protecting the lamp. The iron bars make a beautiful curve to a central point at the top. It looks like a giant bird cage. The windows that were cleaned daily by the keepers no longer exist at Waugoshance. They were probably shattered to pieces by the Lake Michigan storms over the decades. All that remains of the lantern room are the rust-covered iron bars. They look like something from a Tim Burton movie with an old gothic feel to them, like they would be a birdcage for an ominous type of bird such as a vulture or pterodactyl. Looking at it today, i's hard to imagine that at one time a light emitted from the cage and pierced the inky darkness, warning ships of the dangers that lay beneath the water.

In the 1820s, French physicist and engineer Agustin Jean Fresnel came up with a lens made of multiple sections. It focused and magnified a lightsource to project it further. The lens had several sides and was hollow in the middle. A light source, mainly a kerosene lamp, was placed inside the multi-sided lens.

In the early days, a clock-like mechanism would rotate the Fresnel lens. As it rotated, the light shining through the center bullseye would be magnified and seen by the ships' captains and sailors. As the bullseye rotated away, the visible light would disappear, giving the illusion of a flash. The speed of rotation of the light was what determined how fast the lighthouse would blink or "flash". The speed at which the light flashed or didn't flash and the color of the light was known as the characteristic of the light.

Each lighthouse beacon had its own unique characteristic so that captains could identify the lighthouse they were looking at at night. Minot's Ledge Lighthouse off the coast of Cohasset Massachusetts flashes once, then four times, then three times, and has been dubbed the " I Love You" light for the flashes that match up to the number of letters in the romantic phrase.

Chapter 5

Wobbleshanks

I chose July to stay overnight at the old lighthouse because the odds of a storm whipping Lake Michigan into a violent frenzy are low at that time compared to the spring and autumn storms. I wanted to be sure there was a good chance of getting picked up the next day instead of being stranded on this man-made rock for too long. The only problem was it is extremely hot with the midday sun beating down mercilessly on the iron that surrounds the brick. It was like sitting in a black car in the middle of a parking lot. I had a cooler with ice for something cold to drink, but it must have been torture for the keepers. Refrigeration and electricity were not options, so I can only guess if they wanted to keep something cold they had an icebox and maybe got ice from the mainland or from the U.S. Lighthouse supply ship. I was thankful for something cold to drink, but it was going to be a long time before the sun started to set and the air temperature cooled down.

I managed to climb up to the roof of the fog signal structure and was able to find a little bit of shade from the tower while the sun was shining on the opposite side. I hung out sitting there and watched for passing ships as I cooled off from the slight breeze coming across the lake.

Waugoshance 1913

I could see land off in the distance to the east. The shoreline dotted with scrawny pine trees is Point Waugoshance. It reaches out into Lake Michigan and consists of a few islands and is now part of Wilderness State Park. The name Waugoshance is a combination of the word wahgoosh, which is a native American word for fox, and anse, which is French for cove. I guess in simple English, the name means fox cove. Many of the older, seasoned sailors called it "wobbleshanks".

Chapter 6

The Wind

Maybe it was the heat, but looking off in the horizon, I saw what looked like a three-masted schooner. I knew that throughout the summer, several tall ships traveled around the Great Lakes to festivals at different ports.

I often wondered what it was like to sail the Great Lakes back in the day. Yeah, I have been out perch fishing in my dad's little nineteen-foot fiberglass boat, but we never went out too far. Not so far as to lose sight of the shore. I have also taken the trip on the ferry to Mackinac Island a few times. It's a nice little trip across the straits, but it's not what I would call sailing the Great Lakes. It must be a whole different experience relying on the wind to push your ship through the freshwater lakes.

23

To be honest with you, I have never even been on a sailboat. I guess growing up in Saginaw, you get accustomed to being around all the "car guys" and getting addicted to horsepower. When you're young, it's all about going fast and making lots of noise. Now that I am older, I have begun to slow down and enjoy the quiet things in life.

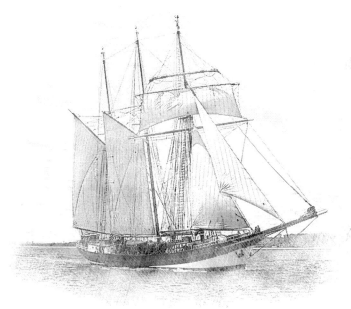

Three Masted Schooner

Using the wind to power a ship seems much more elegant than burning coal or fossil fuels. Just the sails catching an invisible force instead of black smoke billowing out a smokestack. The only problem is that the wind can be so cruel. It must have been frustrating on those days when it did not blow. I imagine for a lowly deckhand, that was an easy day to relax while the captain figured out how he was going to deliver his cargo on time. The worst must have been those days when the wind blew so hard and violently that all they wanted to do was pray for it to stop.

After steam powered ships became more affordable and popular with ship owners, many of the old sailing ships were converted into barges. The masts were removed and a thick rope was tied to the bow and then connected to the stern of a steam-powered ship. Many proud sailing vessels were relegated to being barges and never harnessing the power of the wind. In the worst case, they were cut free during a storm to keep the main ship from being pulled down under the waves.

Chapter 7

Two Holes

While shielding myself from the rays of the sun since I failed to bring any sunscreen, I needed to be careful where I walked on the roof of the fog signal building. It contains two perfectly round holes about two feet in diameter that I didn't want to fall into. My fat gut probably won't pass through, so I would not fall all the way to the floor below, but I definitely would get hurt.

The holes were for two steam pipes. They had whistles on them that the keepers sounded in the fog. When Waugoshance Lighthouse went into operation, it had a bell to ring in the fog. For centuries, bells were used by early lighthouse keepers to help guide mariners in the dense fog. The challenge for the keepers was that someone had to stay at the bell and constantly ring it until the fog cleared. This was solved when someone invented a system to automatically ring the bell. It was a clock-like mechanism with a weight that pulled a rope or cable. It would ring the bell at fifteen or thirty-second intervals. All the keeper had to do was raise the weight once a day, either in the lighthouse tower or a separate building. In times of low visibility, all that needed to be done was release the weight and start the bell ringing and hope the constant ringing did not drive them insane.

One of the problems with using a bell as a signal is that ships used a bell too. The sailors rang bells to keep from colliding with other ships when sailing "blind". Captains could confuse the bell at a lighthouse with another ship. The other issue with a bell is that it was only loud enough to be heard about two miles away. The lighthouse service began experimenting with other types of fog signals and determined that steam whistles were louder than bells. A steam whistle could be heard about eight miles away, depending on what direction the wind was blowing. The steam whistle needed a boiler to operate, which required coal or firewood to generate steam. Lighthouses on land could use the nearby timber for firewood. At Waugoshance, firewood or coal had to be delivered.

Two steam boilers were installed at Waugoshance with pipes and whistles protruding out of the top. That is what the two holes in the roof were used for. They installed two fog signal systems for redundancy so that if one fog signal malfunctioned or was being serviced, the other would be operational. It was a difficult and hot job shoveling coal into the boiler that was confined inside the iron-sheathed brick signal room. I am sure the constant WHOOOOOT!! of the steam signal screeching every thirty seconds would have driven more than one keeper insane.

If you are wondering about the fog horns that you hear in movies and TV shows with the low two-tone BUUUURR-EEEERRRR, they were invented in Canada in the 1920s, so it would not have been used at Waugoshance. Nowadays, fog signals are rarely used with ships having modern technology. Radar, sonar and GPS are used to determine position and enable the ship's pilot to see dangers that are not visible to the human eye in foggy conditions.

Chapter 8
An Ideal Location

You would think just sitting around and watching the waves slowly move across the lake would be relaxing. For a short time, it was calming, but after about ten or twenty minutes, I got bored and my mind started to wander.

I guess that is why lighthouse keepers are required to do so much maintenance when they are on duty. It was the lighthouse service's attempt to minimize keepers from going insane at an isolated lighthouse. Every day they had to clean and polish the lamp and Fresnel lens. They had to carry kerosene up the spiral staircase and fill the reservoir. The keepers were required to have the lamp ready for sunset that evening.

Then there was basic cleaning of the lighthouse and executing the daily chores of cooking, cleaning and laundry, just to name a few. If there was nothing else that needed to be done, the keepers painted anything that needed it, and many times surfaces that didn't, but they did it anyway. Some keepers joked that there was not a square corner anywhere in a lighthouse because they painted so much that all the layers of paint rounded off the corners.

Painting seems like a simple task, and if you are painting your living room, it is. When you have to paint the exterior of a five story round tower, it gets a little tricky. They did not set up scaffolding, and they definitely did not go down to the rental store and get a hydraulic lift. The keepers tied ropes to a board and hung it over the side. I guess if you are an old sailor who is used to climbing around the rigging of a sailing ship, it was not that big of a deal. I am guessing OSHA would not approve of their methods today.

I didn't have any painting to do, but I was getting tired of sitting there waiting for something to happen. I found a broom leaned against a wall at the lighthouse so I started sweeping the floors covered in bits and pieces of old mortar that had fallen out of the walls; it was also mixed in with the bird feathers and dried up excrement. Since I was living there for the day, I was the keeper and it was my responsibility to maintain the old place. I hoped the inspector did not show up with his white gloves and wipe his finger across any horizontal surface, looking for dust. I would have failed that miserably. They have also been known to write down infractions for something as simple as leaving a pan or pot sitting out on the stove. I didn't have to worry about that since I didn't have a stove or even a kitchen.

I read somewhere that if a keeper was stationed at an isolated location for a year, he could choose his next station as long as it was available. It got me thinking as to what would be the best lighthouse on the Great Lakes to be stationed at. My first thought was "Big Red" in Holland. It is a large lighthouse near a big city, and the view of Lake Michigan sunsets would be spectacular. I am thinking a lighthouse near a town would be ideal so you would not have to hike several miles to get supplies.

The lighthouse in Port Sanilac is basically another house in town that has a tower attached to it. But then again, having neighbors who are annoying is not ideal.

Northern Michigan sounds romantic in modern times, but way back before the invention of the automobile, a lighthouse can be isolated rather easily. Driving to Grand Traverse Light by car today can be a long trip from Northport, let alone from Traverse City. A century ago, it must have been nearly impossible to travel through the deep snow during the winter months. Especially before the invention of snowmobiles and trucks with plows.

Back to my original question: where would be the best lighthouse in the Great Lakes to be stationed at? The Little Traverse Lighthouse is in Harbor Springs opposite Petoskey. Most people don't know about the lighthouse because it is privately owned and not open to the public.

The Harbor Springs area has always been a summer resort town for the wealthy Chicago elite. Ephram Shay, who designed a locomotive for logging, had a summer home in Harbor Springs. He built a railroad line to Petoskey so you could get to the "big city" of Petoskey year round.

What about the Mackinac Point Lighthouse? That seems nice, but I am thinking Mackinaw City was more of an industrial town back in the day with all the railroad ferries crossing the straits. Round Island Lighthouse on

Mackinac Island would be nice in the summer and you could take a ferry to the mainland, but in the winter you would be trapped. It's not like you could just jump on a plane and get off the island way back in the early 1900s.

The old lighthouse on Belle Isle is long gone. It was a Queen Ann Victorian style lighthouse, and you would be close to the booming metropolis of Detroit.

I decided I needed to get back to sweeping and cleaning up. I suppose no matter which lighthouse you are stationed at, you still have chores to do and the responsibility of making sure the light is glowing every night all night long.

Chapter 9
Raising the Stars and Stripes

I continued to check my phone for messages. Then I remembered I had absolutely no service. Just a circle with a line through it where the bars of signal strength should have been. For a little while, the idea of no contact with the modern world sounded peaceful. Now it had become a source of anxiety. What if something happened and I didn't know about it? My mind started thinking of the most horrific events to occur. I had to reassure myself that if my family needed to contact me, they would know where I was, and a boat from Mackinaw City would come to retrieve me. It had only been a few hours, but not being able to send or receive messages had been hard to deal with. I also wanted to connect to the internet to check the weather or see what was happening on Facebook. I felt like a drug addict going through withdrawal.

I suppose for the keepers who were stationed at a remote lighthouse the isolation and lack of contact did not hit them as quickly. When the lighthouse was in use, there was no instant form of communication other than good old fashioned snail mail. The telegraph was around back then, but wires were never run to the crib from shore, and wireless was not adopted by the U.S. Lighthouse Service until after the lighthouse was decommissioned. Besides, they did not have electricity for the lighthouse either.

I assume it took a few weeks for the lack of contact to take a toll on their minds. I wished I could check my email right then. Oh well; it would probably just be from a Nigerian prince who wanted to give me money to transfer a vast sum of wealth from his account to a foreign government or something stupid like that.

I waited long enough. I needed to climb the scaffolding to the top of the tower. I went to my backpack and pulled out a small American flag. It was stapled to a wooden stick like the kind you would see stuck into the ground next to a headstone of a veteran laid to rest in a cemetery. I figured since I was going to be "stationed" at the lighthouse, I would fly the Stars and Stripes over it. I put the flag in my back pocket and a few zip ties in my front pocket.

I grabbed the steel bar that was welded as part of the framework. The yellow paint has been mostly worn off. Over the years, workers' hands and boots have slowly scuffed the paint away from the steel. Some of the original paint has been replaced by splatters of paint, most likely from painters in white overalls painting drywall on construction sites. It was mostly now covered in a light coat of rust sitting out there on a man-made concrete island.

I squeezed down tight on one of the rungs and gave the structure a shake. It squeaked and rattled, but it seemed sturdy. I put my foot up on the first rung and pulled myself up. I worked my way up to the next level. There are about six levels total with old two by eight pine planking on each level. I got up another level and climbed onto the planking to look out the small square opening where a glass window once kept the wind from blowing into the tower. The planking was not that sturdy; as I got to the center it was rather bouncy when I stood on it, looking out over Lake Michigan.

I climbed back onto the built-in ladder on the scaffolding framework. As the tower narrowed toward the top, it was a tight fit between the scaffolding and the bricks. My back scraped the wall as I pulled my way up a few more levels. The higher I climbed, the more rickety the scaffolding became. It swayed as I leaned out to reach up and grab the next bar over my head. As I rose to the top, the scaffolding felt like it could topple over if I leaned out too far. Being confined inside the tower, I was sure it would not fall over.

I finally made it to the top level. Wood planking covered the top and was about three or four feet from the metal floor where the lantern once stood. A small opening in the rusty metal framework allowed for a keeper to enter the lantern room. It would have been where the spiral staircase ended. Now it was an opening for me to stand up and look through.

I grabbed hold of some metal brackets bolted to the floor and pulled myself up, lifting my knee onto the opening and pushing up with my leg like I was getting out of a swimming pool. I was finally at the top of the lighthouse, and I stood up in the bird cage style lantern room. The view was breathtaking, with waves rippling on the clear waters of Lake Michigan. I could see down to the rocks underneath the surface. I could also see the rubble which used to be part of the concrete crib that had been pummeled by the winter ice. It slowly chewed into the walls and was pulling the base of the lighthouse back into the lake.

Birds flew around in the clear blue summer sky. I was sure they were circling around looking at me and wondering why I was in their favorite place to rest while they looked over the water for fish. I know they liked it there because I could see all the white streaks of bird dung underneath the iron railing. It was funny that the so-called bird cage that was once home to the lantern that guided sailors and ships through the straits was now home to the birds.

Between the rust and the excrement covering most everything, it was not a place for me to hang out too long. I zipped tied my cemetery flag to the railing and watched as it waved in a light breeze. I would have preferred a "real" flag, but this was the least I could do to honor the men and women who faithfully served in the lighthouse and the military. Now that the "Stars and Stripes" were waving over Waugoshance, I could shimmy my way back down to the bottom of the tower.

Chapter 10

Island Orphans

I had a gnawing feeling in the back of my mind that I was trapped on the crumbling concrete island. I was used to having my Jeep nearby. Even though I may not have wanted to, I could have jumped into it and driven to my heart's content. It might have been just going to the store to get some stuff, or I could have driven for days looking for freedom on the open road.

When the lighthouse was in operation, it had a pair of small crane-like devices called davits that could raise and lower a boat in and out of the water. Keepers could sail into town to get supplies or at the very least, some social interaction.

Sailing a small boat on the open water of the Great Lakes is not as easy as driving to the local 7-Eleven for a slurpee. The death of Keeper Sheridan and his wife and baby are proof of how dangerous it can be.

Aaron Sheridan served the Union Army in the Civil War. He was shot in the arm during the Battle of Ringgold, and it had to be amputated in the field to save his life. After the war, he returned home to work on the farm. He was not able to make much of a living working a farm with only one arm.

He found out from his cousin that the keeper at South Manitou Island had left and there was a vacancy for a new keeper. He petitioned the government for the position. It was customary for the U.S. government to give lighthouse jobs to military veterans, especially those wounded in battle. In 1866, Aaron Sheridan was given the position of head lighthouse keeper, even though he had no experience as a keeper or sailor and never served time in the navy. Nonetheless, he and his wife, Julia, and children moved to South Manitou Island.

South and North Manitou Islands are about ten miles offshore from the Leelanau Peninsula. Between them is the Manitou Passage and a popular "short cut" for ships traveling north and south on Lake Michigan. The passage was a narrow channel of deep water, and it was easy for ships to get off course and run aground. To help guide captains through the passage, the first of three lighthouses was constructed on South Manitou Island in 1839. A lightship was anchored in 1907 to mark the

South Manitou Lighthouse

dangerous shoal near North Manitou Island. By 1935, a permanent crib light was built and manned by three men. It was automated in 1980, and recently it has been converted to a solar powered LED light. I wonder what the ole wickies would have thought of today's modern technology.

The Sheridans had six children and lived on the island for over a decade, taking care of the lighthouse until their tragic death. On March 15, 1878, Aaron, Julia and their infant son Robert were riding in a small boat back to the island captained by fisherman Chris Ankerson. A sudden squall capsized the small boat, tossing everyone on board into the icy water. Ankerson clung to the overturned boat, but Aaron Sheridan, with only one arm, swam out to rescue his wife and child. He managed to get Julia to the upside down boat, but she was not able to hang on in the rough water. She slipped below the water, and her loving husband once again swam out to rescue her, only to perish himself.

When Ankerson made it back to the island, he told Katherine Hutzler, who was watching the Sheridan children, ages three to twelve, what had happened. The distraught children ran up and down South Manitou Island's beach searching for their parents and little brother. Sadly, their parents and brother were never seen again. The children were taken to Illinois and raised by their grandparents.

One of Aaron and Julia's sons, along with two of their grandsons, became lighthouse keepers on the Great Lakes. After their harrowing ordeal, I am not sure why, but I guess it was as they say "in their blood".

Chapter 11

Target Practice

Looking up at the walls of this once great lighthouse, I can see some of the locations where it was struck by ordinance dropped by airplanes. It is hard to believe the United States Navy used this place for target practice. Although I must admit it is a fascinating story that is mostly forgotten about.

It goes back to the days when the Navy wanted to train pilots to take off and land from aircraft carriers. During World War II, they were not able to do it on the Pacific or Atlantic oceans for fear of German U-boats. The inland seas of the Great Lakes made for a perfect place for training far inland from any enemy interference. The *USS Wolverine* and the *USS Sable* were built in 1942 from old sidewheel luxury steamers the *Seeandbee* and the *Greater Buffalo*. The two ships originally carried passengers on sightseeing cruises around the Great Lakes. Their upper decks were removed and converted into large flat runways. The ships sailed out of Chicago, and many Navy pilots were trained to land on the decks of these two makeshift aircraft carriers.

The Navy also had a secret experimental drone program that operated in the Grand Traverse Bay from the Grand Traverse Naval Air Station, which is now Cherry Capital Airport. The program initially started in Clinton

U.S.S. Wolverine

45

Oklahoma. After learning of the British Royal Navy using remote controlled bi-planes for target practice, the U.S. Navy wondered if unmanned airplanes could be used in combat. Television maker RCA developed technology that enabled a plane to have a camera mounted in the nose while a piloted chase plane could have a television monitor mounted in the cockpit for a pilot to fly the drone remotely.

The first unmanned aerial vehicle (UAV) or drones by the navy were called torpedo drones (TD-1). They were referred to as torpedoes because they would be guided bombs in the air, similar to the way torpedoes were guided bombs in the water. Once the drones were successful in flying from land, they needed to be tested on aircraft carriers. That is when the program was moved to the naval air station in Traverse City. The unmanned aircraft flew practice flights over the Grand Traverse Bay. Civilians in the city were unaware of the secret program and were shocked to see an airplane crash into the water and the military not trying to save the pilot. They did not know that the plane was flown remotely and that it was a test flight.

For further testing, the drones were flown from the *USS Sable* in the Straits of Mackinac where they used the abandoned Waugoshance Lighthouse for a target. At first, they dropped sacks of flour on the old lighthouse, but later, they dropped live bombs, which set the old lighthouse ablaze. Anything that was combustible was turned to ash by the fire.

Before the end of World War II, the flying torpedoes successfully sank a Japanese ship in the Pacific. At the end of the war, the drone program was terminated, and it was decades later that drones were used by the military in combat again.

Chapter 12

Refuge in a Blizzard

I was sitting on the roof of the fog signal room, watching a freighter off in the distance sailing over the horizon. The horizon is the line created by the curvature of the earth. Someone standing on the shoreline can see about three miles to the horizon. The curvature of the earth is the reason why lighthouses have towers. The higher the elevation, the further you can see. It is also true for light traveling from the lighthouse. Because light travels in a straight line, a sailor loses sight of the source of the light as they sail away from it. It is for this reason that some lighthouses have tall towers. Lighthouses that sit on a cliff high above the water usually do not have a tall tower.

The tallest lighthouse on the Great Lakes is the White Shoal Lighthouse on the western end of the Straits of Mackinac. The tower was completed in 1910 and is 121 feet tall. Two years after the beacon went into service, Waugoshance was decommissioned and left abandoned. The White Shoal Lighthouse sits on a man-made crib in the open waters of Lake Michigan. It was a marvel of engineering when it was completed. It was one of a handful of lighthouses on the Great Lakes that had a second order Fresnel lens. When the light was automated in 1975, the lens was removed and put on display at the Whitefish Point Shipwreck Museum. The most notable feature was the red and white "candy cane" helical stripes painted on the exterior of the tower. Because of its aesthetics, an image of the White Shoal Lighthouse was used on the State of Michigan license plates "Save our Lights" campaign.

During a winter storm in 1929, a fifty-four-year-old ice fisherman ended up at White Shoal Lighthouse seeking refuge. Lewis Sweet and a couple buddies came up from the Petoskey area to ice fish near Waugoshance Point. After each one of them cut a large hole in the ice, they set up their ice shanty and used spears to stab any trout that swam past. The prevailing wind blew from the west and kept the ice on Lake Michigan pushed up along the shoreline. The men knew that if the wind shifted to the east, it could drive the ice away from land.

After fishing most of the day, the men noticed a storm off in the distance. The two other fishermen Sweet had been fishing with headed back for shore. Lewis decided he wanted to fish for a few more minutes. After trying to spear one more trout, Lewis grabbed his trout and the axe he used for chopping a hole in the ice and headed back to shore. Lewis heard a thunderous sound echoing across the ice, and he knew instantly that the ice had cracked. He ran as fast as he could in the snow, but when he got to the crack, it was already too wide for him to jump across.

He headed back toward his shanty as the snow began to fall. It came down so heavy that he was not able to see far and could not find his shanty. He knew he needed protection from the wind, so he built a wall from the hard packed snow and lay behind it to block the wind. He got up every few minutes and moved around to keep his body warm. He heard another crack and knew the large chuck of ice that kept him out of the freezing cold water was slowly breaking up. He continued toward what he thought was the center of the ice floe and built another snow wall for shelter. He drifted on the disintegrating hunk of ice throughout the night.

By the next morning, the ice had drifted into the twelve-story-tall White Shoal Lighthouse. The ladder used by the keepers to climb the twenty feet to the cribbing was covered in a thick coating of ice. Sweet used his axe to chop through the thick ice that had coated the ladder. He spent hours chopping, only to reveal about half of the ladder. He then got the idea to stack up the chunks of ice that had broken up when the flow slammed into the lighthouse. He finally made it to the base of the tower. The door was unlocked, and he took refuge in the relative safety of the lighthouse.

Inside the lighthouse, Lewis found kerosene and a heater along with some food he could eat. He finally managed to get warmed up. His feet and hands were blistered and frostbitten from the cold. He could hear an airplane flying overhead. By the time he climbed the stairs on his injured feet to signal the plane, it was already out of sight. He had

White Shoal Lighhthouse

enough rations in the lighthouse to keep him alive for over a month, but he knew he needed to seek medical attention for his feet.

After a few days, Lake Michigan had once again frozen over. He was not sure if he could make it back to shore, but Sweet took the chance anyways. He grabbed some rations for the trip, which included a can of condensed milk. He used a rope to lower himself down to the frozen surface of the lake. In agony, he trekked across the ice back to land. He had managed to hike nearly twenty miles when he made landfall near Cross Village, where he found an old hunting cabin.

He built a fire in the stove and found some leftover coffee and brewed himself a cup where he poured in some of his condensed milk. After drinking his coffee, he lay down to rest. He woke up to terrible pains in his stomach and wondered if the condensed milk had gone bad.

He spent the next day recouping from whatever ailed him and finally was healthy enough to search for civilization. He hiked through the snow towards Cross Village, where some Native American girls spotted him stumbling out of the forest. Scared, the girls quickly ran home, and someone finally came out to get Lewis Sweet.

He was taken by dog sled to the nearby town of Levering and then driven by car to the hospital in Petoskey. All of his toes were amputated and most of his fingers. He was in the hospital for ten weeks. Limited in what he could do for work, his story was published in a book with the proceeds going to support him and his family.

Sitting out here at Waugoshance and thinking of the ordeal that Lewis Sweet went through to get back home made me hope that Captain Bob did not forget about me.

Chapter 13

My Friend Jonathan

My stomach began rumbling, so I figured now was a good time to make some sandwiches with the stuff I had packed in my cooler. I didn't have a dining table or any furniture to sit at and eat supper. I figured I would make do with sitting on my cot and using my plastic cooler as a table.

For the most part, the gulls and other birds have been keeping their distance. I was sure they were used to having the lighthouse all to themselves. It was on rare occasions they had to deal with human intervention. One seagull seemed particularly brave, coming closer and closer to me as I ate. Without anyone to talk to, I named him Jonathan. I thought about Jason for the guy who played Marshall on

How I Met Your Mother, but I went with Jonathan. It sounded more formal, and that is the name from one of my favorite books, *Jonathan Livingston Seagull*. I was contemplating if I should reward Jonathan with a piece of bread. I was worried that as soon as the other birds saw me feeding one of their own, they would swoop down, expecting the same. Then it would be a melee like two people fighting over a big screen TV on Black Friday.

"What's the word in the sky, Jonathan? Do you think the weather will be nice tonight?"

He just looked at me and did not say anything.

"Thank you for joining me for dinner."

When you are used to eating almost every meal with your family, it is strange eating alone. When I am eating by myself at a restaurant, I am looking at my smartphone. Not that there is anything of great interest; it just feels weird looking around a public dining room while I'm eating. I definitely don't want to get caught looking at other people eating and be that "creepy guy" sitting alone.

"How's the wife and kids? Are they back at the nest while you are out exploring the lake?"

Legend has it that seagulls are the souls of sailors or fishermen who have drowned. It is also believed that seagulls warn captains of an incoming storm.

"Are you trying to tell me something Jonathan? I checked the weather app on my phone before I left this morning, and it called for nice weather tonight."

Too bad I couldn't check it right then. Maybe if I had cell service I would not have been talking to a seagull.

I broke off a small piece of bread from my sandwich and tossed it next to the cooler. I tried to place it out of sight from the other birds. I figured it was impolite of me to eat and not offer a little something to my guest. He slowly walked closer and closer to the cooler. I slid over a little bit on my cot to give him some distance. He gobbled up the small piece of bread and flew away.

"That is Spatz bread. If you like it, you will have to fly to Saginaw to get some if you want more!" I yelled as he went up over the wall of the lighthouse.

I grew up in Saginaw, Michigan, and anyone who has lived there knows the Spatz Bakery. They have been baking homemade bread for over a century and a half. I know many people who have moved away from Saginaw, and they stop and get a few loaves every time they are back in town visiting relatives. I wonder if Jonathan will be back for more. He will have to fly to Saginaw to get some after I leave Waugoshance.

Chapter 14

Light From a Wick

As the earth rotated and the sun became lower in the sky, I knew that it would not be long and darkness would fall across Lake Michigan. I needed to get up to the top of the tower and get a light going to warn any nearby sailors. Not that they needed it in this modern era, but I thought since I was the head keeper of Waugoshance, it was my duty to keep the light on. I grabbed a candle, a long stemmed lighter that I called a "clicker", and a battery powered led camping lantern.

I climbed up the scaffolding to the lantern room. Old

Glory was still zip-tied to the iron bar and waving in the light breeze. I got out my lantern and turned on the light. I tested it at home a few nights ago, and the batteries lasted all night, so I was sure the light would shine through the night. I also brought a candle in honor of all the "wickies" who worked in the days before electricity.

In the early days of the lighthouse during ancient times, a fire made with wood at the top of a tower was the primary source for warning captains of danger. The

Fresnel Lens

burning wood did not produce a consistent flame and had to be continuously maintained throughout the night. The next progression was the use of candles. The United States' first lighthouse in Boston, built in the early 1700s, used candles made by the lighthouse keepers from tallow. The keepers lit multiple candles and enclosed them in glass to keep the wind from extinguishing them.

By the late 1700s, lighthouses began using fish or whale oil and sometimes oil rendered from animal fat. The early lamps were simple pans with multiple wicks. In 1782, Franqois Pierre Ami Argand, a Swiss born physicist living in France, came up with a design for an oil lamp which burned brighter. He had a circular wick with a round glass "chimney" that pulled air up through it, causing the wick to burn brighter without flickering. Later on, a polished piece of metal was added to the back side to reflect the light. Known as Argand lamps, multiple ones were used in lighthouse lantern rooms to warn passing ships.

By the 1860s, most lighthouses had begun using petroleum kerosene instead of whale oil. By the late 1800s, it was discovered that the kerosene could be pressurized and forced out of a nozzle as a gas. A silk mantle was placed over the nozzle, and it created a brilliant light. If you have ever used an old Coleman camping lantern that used Coleman fuel, you are familiar with the process. The kerosene lamp along with the Fresnel lens was the way many of the early Great Lakes lighthouses were illuminated.

Electricity became the next form of illumination after Thomas Edison perfected the light bulb in the early 1900s. Lighthouses near large cities made the transformation to electricity, but many lighthouses continued using kerosene lamps. Because of their isolation, it was easier to use the older, more reliable lamps than either run electricity to the lighthouse or operate a generator. We take for granted how easy it is to flip a switch or plug into a wall outlet and have reliable electricity. It was not so simple in the early 1900s.

Now that I was at the top of Waugoshance's tower, I turned on my LED lantern and placed it on the railing. I had also brought a candle with me to light in honor of all the "wickies" who had maintained the light through the darkness of night. I pulled the trigger——click click click—nothing. I gave it a shake, then click click click. Still nothing. "Ah, com'on, you stupid thing!" I yelled. A few birds flew away, and I pulled the trigger again. Click! I got a little flame. I lit the candle and placed it on the floor of the old lantern room, and climbed my way back down the scaffolding.

Chapter 15
Sunset

I was sitting on top of the fog signal roof again, watching the sun set over Lake Michigan. I still had that instinct to reach down and look at my phone. I didn't have any service, but I sent a text to my wife. Doing great at the lighthouse. Love you. Goodnight. I hit the send button, and the little circle that indicated it was sending just spinned hopelessly.

It was so strange to be there without any communication. I had no idea what was happening in the world as I sat there isolated from all information. Did the stock market crash? Did aliens from outer space land in the desert? Or maybe a pandemic had swept around the globe. They say ignorance is bliss, and not knowing the latest news wasn't too bad, but wondering about my family was the hard part. I figured if something tragic were to happen, they would send someone out to find me.

I wonder how the old keepers handled the isolation. There was no radio or daily newspaper to let them know what was happening in the world. It was their daily chores that kept them busy and their minds from wandering. It must have been especially challenging for the men stationed at the offshore lighthouses. At least on the land-based lighthouses, they had some land to get out for a walk. Or maybe a garden to grow some vegetables.

The United States Lighthouse Service did have a few tenders that traveled the Great Lakes replenishing supplies. The first ship specifically built to be a lighthouse tender was the *USLTH Dahlia*. The 125-foot ship was built in 1874 and sailed from Detroit to supply the lighthouse that could not be reached easily by land. Besides replenishing kerosene for the lamp and food for the keepers, it also provided a connection to the outside world. The tender also transported small wooden trunks with books for keepers to read. These "trunk libraries" would be picked up and exchanged from one lighthouse to another, continuously rotating books for keepers and their families to read. That was probably the closest thing they had to Netflix way back before the internet or the television was invented.

The sun was close to the horizon and would soon disappear from view. There were a few clouds in the sky and a ship in the distance. The breeze off the lake was getting cooler. Hopefully, it would be a nice night for sleeping.

Chapter 16

The Stars

Lying on top of my sleeping bag on my portable cot, I could see a glow in the old bird cage at the top of Waugoshaunce's tower. I could also see the stars shining in the night sky. The same stars that were twinkling centuries ago to guide sailors on their voyages. It must have taken great skill and years of training to be able to navigate by the stars. All I have to do is punch in an address on my smartphone and it will take me to my destination and even tell me the traffic conditions. Although I still have difficulty getting directions on my phone in the Upper Peninsula when I don't have a cell signal. I guess that is what it must have been like when the clouds covered up the stars.

In the early days of sailing the Great Lakes, most sailors relayed on landmarks to determine their locations. Such as the Manitou Islands or the tip of Michigan's Thumb. This worked well during the day, but at night, the lighthouses constructed along the shoreline let captains know their approximate location. It was not until the Second World War that Radio Detection And Ranging, or as most people call it RADAR, was added to ships, diminishing the need for lighthouses, but they were still used as a backup and relied on by vessels not equipped with the latest technology.

While radar was used to "see" the surroundings of a ship, location was done using Long Range Navigation, known as LORAN. It used a system of radio towers and signals to calculate the longitude and latitude position on the earth's surface. It worked similar to the way GPS uses satellites to calculate location, only LORAN was only accurate to a few hundred feet. It was popular from the 1950s until the 1980s when GPS became available. The interesting fact about LORAN was that the main radio tower was at a station run by the Coast Guard in the middle of Indiana. That would be kind of strange to be a coastie and be stationed among the cornfields of the midwest.

Chapter 17

The Storm

I woke up to the sound of waves crashing against the worn concrete cribbing and water splashing through the windows. The wind made an eerie howling sound as it whipped around the old brick and iron walls. I quickly grabbed my cot, sleeping bag and other belongings, and hightailed it to the protective cover of the fog signal room. I glanced up at the tower, and the light I had placed at dusk was no longer glowing. I heard thunder rumbling in the distance, and large drops of rain began to fall. A few seconds later, the sky opened up and rain poured down while lightning flashed over Lake Michigan. So much for the weather report saying it was going to be nice weather that night.

I was the keeper of Waugoshance, and it was my duty to keep the light on. I grabbed my little flashlight and went over to the tower. I clenched the flashlight in my teeth and started climbing the scaffolding as water came down from the windowless bird cage lantern room. The wet steel bars were difficult to grip, but I pulled myself up one rung at a time.

I was about halfway to the top when my left foot slipped off the rung and my shin slammed into the cold, hard steel. I don't know if you have ever walked into a trailer hitch striking out of the back bumper of a truck, but that is what it felt like. I gritted my teeth and grunted, trying not to drop the flashlight. I stopped for a minute and held on with my right hand and pulled the light out of my mouth with my left hand. I stood there breathing hard and looking up at the top of the tower where there should have been light. It was dark except for a few flashes of light from the lightning as the raging storm passed over the old lighthouse one more time.

The throbbing in my leg calmed down a little, and I put the flashlight back in my mouth and started climbing again, ascending the scaffolding using my right leg to do the heavy work of pulling my body up and then stabilizing myself with my left leg. Part of me wanted to quit and go back down to my cot, but I had to get the light back on for all the keepers that came before me.

I made it to the opening at the top in the lantern room. I poked my head out, and the wind blasted me in the face like a dog striking its head out the car window on the expressway. I squinted my eyes and looked around to see that my lantern had blown over and then turned off. The candle had blown out too. I grabbed the lantern and gave it a shake, and the light came back on. When it fell over, the battery must have gotten disconnected, but it was working again. I placed it back on the deck of the birdcage and got back into the safety of the tower. I figured there was no way I was going to get the candle to stay lit, so I started my descent back down the scaffolding.

It was slow and wet as water poured down from the top of the tower. I carefully climbed down, not wanting to have a repeat accident and bang my badly bruised shin against a metal rung. Eventually, I reached the bottom of

71

the tower and looked up to see the light glowing through the opening as I took the flashlight from my mouth. Even though the storm raged on, I went outside to the edge of the former keeper's house, I looked up where the roof had been to see the light from my little lantern glowing in the old bird cage. I know there was no logical reason for the light in this day of modern navigation, but it brought me a sense of accomplishment and a little life to this long abandoned lighthouse.

Chapter 18

A Disabled Veteran

I went back into the fog signal room and stripped off most of my wet clothes. It was still warm inside with the bricks holding the heat from the day's sunshine. I sat down on my cot and shone the light on my shin. It was scraped up but not bleeding.

I was not the first to brave a storm to keep the light shining. Keeper Donahue at South Haven light was known for his bravery and tenacity. James S. Donahue rose to the rank of Captain in the Union Army during the Civil War. He lost a leg at the Battle of Wilderness and retired from active duty. In need of a job, he applied for duty as a lighthouse keeper. After learning of his disability, he was denied a position as a lighthouse keeper.

73

He responded, requesting that he be given a chance. The lighthouse board honored his request in 1884 and gave him the position of head keeper at the Grand Haven Lighthouse.

It was a typical southern Michigan lighthouse on the Lake Michigan shoreline. The tower was placed at the end of a pier with a catwalk that ran the length of the pier. The keeper's house was further inland, and they had to walk every day from the house to the light at the end of the pier.

I think the Lighthouse Board chose that light for Donahue, figuring he would not be able to make the difficult trek to maintain the light. The 32-year-old keeper proved them wrong and held onto his job for 36 years, making the trip to the lighthouse in all kinds of weather from hot summer nights to the most ferocious of late autumn storms with the catwalk covered in ice and snow and pummeled by gale force winds. James Donahue also saved over a dozen sailors' lives, rescuing them from the icy waters of Lake Michigan. Having a missing leg never seemed to slow him down. They say his ghost haunts the old keeper's house in South Haven. It is now home to the Marialyce Canonie Great Lakes Research Library, operated by the Michigan Maritime Museum. The staff have claimed to hear strange thumping sounds and believe it is the ghost of James S. Donahue's crutches and that his spirit roams his former home.

South Haven Pierhead Light 1932

Chapter 19

Keepers' Ghosts

Most of Michigan's lighthouses have a lot of history associated with them, and along with that history comes some tragic and strange stories.

The Seul Choix Point Lighthouse stands near the town of Gulliver on the northern shore of Lake Michigan in the Upper Peninsula. Seul Choix, pronounced sis shwa, is French for "only choice" because it is the only harbor of refuge between Escanaba and Saint Ignace.

Stories from some of the volunteers and visitors claim the historic lighthouse is haunted by a former keeper who served the structure from 1902 until his death In 1910. It is said that he passed away while in the bedroom that is located upstairs. His name was Joseph Willie Townsend.

He and his wife resided in the house, and he was known to enjoy smoking cigars. Unfortunately, his wife was not a huge fan of the smell and smoke associated with the cigars and informed him that he could not smoke them in the house.

Since his death, many people have claimed to smell burning cigars in the house. It's believed that Townsend purposely smokes in the house in the afterlife as his wife cannot forbid it now. People have also claimed to have seen Townsend's Ghost roaming around in the residential part of the lighthouse and that furniture is rearranged during the night.

Another strange occurrence is that the forks on the table mysteriously change position. Although the dining room table is set with dishes and silverware, with the forks' tines facing up, the forks are turned tine side down when nobody is watching. Townsend was known to set his forks down in that position.

Keeper Townsend is not the only keeper suspected of haunting the lighthouse he lived in. William Robinson was appointed as the first keeper of the White River Lighthouse, located at the mouth of the White River, north of Muskegon. After it was built in 1875, Keeper

Robinson and his wife Sarah moved into the little brick lighthouse, where they raised their thirteen children. William Robinson was the head keeper for 47 years, at which time the Lighthouse Board decided that since he was 87 years old, the assistant keeper should take over the duties of maintaining the lighthouse. The assistant keeper was William Bush, and he was Robinson's grandson. A few days before Bush officially took over the duties of running the lighthouse, his grandfather William peacefully died in the lighthouse that he loved and worked at for so many years. It is said that he and his wife's spirits still remain at the lighthouse, watching over it.

Eagle Harbor is located on the western side of the Keweenaw Peninsula in the Upper Peninsula. Its rocky harbor made for a safe refuge from the many storms that swept over Lake Superior. In the 1850s, a lighthouse and life-saving station was constructed near the entrance of the natural harbor.

Stephen Cocking became the lighthouse keeper in 1877. He was born in England in 1836, and at the age of eleven, he emigrated to the United States and came to work in the copper mines in the Keweenaw Peninsula. After serving in the Civil War in the 23rd Michigan Volunteer Infantry

Regiment, he moved back to the Upper Peninsula. He was the keeper at Eagle Harbor until he died at the lighthouse of pneumonia in 1889.

In 1962, the lighthouse was converted to an electric light and automated. In the 1970s, a Coast Guardsman who was stationed at Eagle Harbor Lighthouse for three years told of his strange paranormal encounters. While living at the lighthouse during the night, he heard what sounded like furniture being dragged across the floor of the second-story bedroom. The light switch on the main floor would mysteriously click on and off. He would see light coming from under the door on the main floor to the tower, but when he opened it, the light would disappear, only to reappear when he closed it! On one occasion, a guest staying in the upstairs bedroom left in the morning, frightened and claiming to have seen a ghost in a plaid shirt without a face.

The Coastie moved to the white house used by the US Lifesaving Service next to the lighthouse, hoping it would be quieter. He said that house was even more haunted. While sleeping on the second floor, he would hear footsteps downstairs that would go up the stairs, down the hall and stop at the door to his bedroom. He would be woken in the middle of the night by strange voices. No one knows for sure, but I wonder if former Keeper Stephen Cocking is the cantankerous spirit roaming the lighthouse?

Eagle Harbor Lighthouse

Chapter 20

The Sky Pilot

I woke to the sunlight glowing from the two round holes in the roof of the fog signal room. I went outside just in time to see the sun rising over the trees on the shoreline of Wilderness State Park. It was a beautiful morning and nothing like the thunderstorm that had passed through in the night. I sat my chair in the doorway and watched as the sun rose slowly into the sky.

It would be nice to have some bacon and eggs for breakfast, but I guessed I would have to wait until I got back on shore. I would just sit there and eat one of my protein bars and read a little.

I am sure the keepers spent a lot of their downtime reading. It's not like they could just log onto Netflix in the 1800s. The lighthouse service did have wooden crates filled with books. They were little libraries that they would exchange with other lighthouses during supply visits. Unfortunately, the little library trunks were not a priority, and over time the books became outdated and ragged. The lighthouse service's main priority was the navigation of ships and not necessarily the well-being of the lighthouse keepers and their families.

It was a mishap during a northern Lake Huron storm that changed a minister's mission to provide comfort and aid for lighthouse keepers and the men of the US Life Saving Service.

Reverend William H. Law was a minister who lived in the Upper Peninsula town of Hessel in the Les Cheneaux Island Chain. Around 1900, he and his son visited a friend on Bois Blanc Island, located in Lake Huron near Mackinac Island. On their return trip to Hessel, they encountered a storm, and the waves pushed the small boat against the rocks along the shoreline of Bois Blanc Island. When the men of the U.S. Lifesaving Service, stationed on the island, saw him and his boat in peril on the rocks, they immediately launched a surfboat. They rowed through the waves to save the reverend and his son. The men quickly tied a rope to the Reverend's boat and rowed back to the station, where they sheltered and fed William and his son.

As the storm raged on for the next few days, the reverend and his son remained at the station with the men and their families. Learning of their low pay and isolation, he found his calling and dedicated the rest of his life to helping them. Reverend Law collected books for the keepers along with toys and crafts for their children. During the summer months, he would sail the Great Lakes, visiting all of the lighthouses and lifesaving stations with what he called his "floating library". During the winter months, he would lobby Congress to improve the working conditions and pay for the men and women who kept the lights on. He helped in the passing of legislation that would give the keepers pensions after they retired from their duties.

The reverend brought much joy and comfort to many keepers and their families. He was known as the Sky Pilot of the Great Lakes. "Sky Pilot" is slang that sailors used for a chaplain. He continued his dedication to the families of the Life Saving Service until his death in 1928. Since Waugoshance Lighthouse was deactivated in 1910, I am sure the Reverend stopped by a few times to give the keeper some books to read and some much needed contact with the outside world.

Chapter 21

The First Two

Waugoshance was the first lighthouse to be built on the great lakes completely surrounded by water, but it was not the first lighthouse. Two lighthouses share the distinction of being the first on the Great Lakes. After the War of 1812, a lighthouse was constructed in 1818 by the US government at the mouth of the Buffalo River where it empties into Lake Erie. Another lighthouse was constructed at the same time at Erie Pennsylvania to mark the entrance to Erie Bay located between Buffalo and Cleveland. The Buffalo light was a stone tower about 35 feet tall with a log cabin for a keeper's house. It was replaced by a more capable beacon in 1826. The Erie Bay lighthouse stood until 1858 but had to be replaced because it was built on unstable ground and began to collapse.

The oldest lighthouse still standing on the Great Lakes is the Marblehead Lighthouse on Lake Erie in Ohio. It stands at the tip of Marblehead Point and marks the

Marblehead Lighthouse

entrance of Sandusky Bay. It was constructed in 1821 from limestone quarried nearby. The base of the fifty foot tall tower is twenty-five feet in diameter, and the walls are five feet thick. The first keeper was Revolutionary War veteran Benjah Walcot. He lived in the keeper's house built near the tower and lit the thirteen whale oil lamps every night. After his death in 1832, his wife Rachel took over the responsibility of lighting the lamps and maintaining the lighthouse.

The light was automated in 1958, and a keeper was no longer needed at the historic lighthouse. The Ohio Department of Natural Resources took over maintaining the lighthouse and a state park was created on the land surrounding the beacon and is a popular destination for tourists.

Chapter 22

A Brave Woman

Rachel Walcott was one of the nation's first female lighthouse keepers. Although she was never considered an official keeper, she was allowed to continue with the duties of lightkeeper until a replacement was found or she remarried. Which she did, and her second husband became the official keeper.

The first official female lighthouse keeper in the U.S. was Maria Andreu. She was a Hispanic-American who became the first woman to command a federal shore installation when she took command in January 1860 of St Augustine Lighthouse in Florida when her husband, who was the head keeper, died while whitewashing the tower. She was only keeper for about a year when the light was ordered to stay off by the Confederate States Secretary of the Navy.

Andreu moved to Georgia and never went back to being a lighthouse keeper.

Michigan has had a few notable female lighthouse keepers, not including the wives of keepers who received little recognition for their commitment to keep the light shining at night. One of the most notable female lighthouse keepers was Harriet Colfax. She was the keeper of the Michigan City Lighthouse in Indiana. She came to the Hoosier State in the 1850s with her brother when they were both in their twenties. Her brother was an editor of a newspaper, and she worked for him as a typesetter. After his sudden death, she needed a job.

The first lighthouse in Michigan City was constructed in 1858, and she applied for a position as lightkeeper. You know the old saying: "It's who you know and not what you know". That was the case with Harriet. Her cousin Schuyler Colfax was the Representative for Indiana in the House of Representative. He was a successful and influential politician who eventually worked his way up to Speaker of the House and was vice president under Ulysses S. Grant. At the time, lighthouse keepers were appointed by the politicians in Washington D.C., and Schuyler arranged Harriet's appointment.

It is unclear that he ever mentioned that she was a woman, but Harriet became one of Michigan's most respected keepers. She tended the lights on the east and west piers for forty-three years. It was no easy task. Every night she had to row out to the light with kerosene fuel and light the lamp. She did this in all kinds of weather, from torrential thunderstorms in the spring to blinding snow storms and icy waves in the winter. She had help from her childhood friend Ann C. Hartwell, who lived with her in the Southern Lake Michigan Lighthouse. The two women retired in 1904 after decades of service and moved out of the government owned lighthouse they had called home. About a year later, Ann died, and Harriet followed a few months later. The two women are buried next to each other in Michigan City's Greenwood Cemetery.

Chapter 23

The Range Lights

My stomach was beginning to rumble because it had been a while since I had had anything to eat. It wouldn't be long until Captain Bob would be there in the *Ships Ahoy*. I was looking forward to going back to my hometown of Saginaw and taking a shower and sleeping in my own bed.

Growing up in Saginaw along the Saginaw River was where I got my love of the Great Lakes. My dad had a nineteen-foot fiberglass boat that we would launch along the river. We would travel up the river through Bay City and out the mouth of the river and into Saginaw Bay.

Near the mouth of the river stands the old rear range Saginaw River Lighthouse. It is known as a range light because it consisted of two beacons—one in front and another a distance away in back. When a sailor aligns the two lights on top of one another, they know they are headed in a safe direction, usually in a channel dredged in a bay or harbor.

The range lights came about because of the ingenuity of keeper Peter Brawn's (sometimes listed as Peter Brown) son Dewit. In the 1860s, when he was not helping his physically challenged father at the lighthouse, he enjoyed sailing his small boat around Saginaw Bay. To help find his way back to the mouth of the river, he would line up two landmarks on shore. This gave him the idea of placing two lights on shore for ship captains to align.

Saginaw Bay had a long narrow channel leading into the river. At night, ships heading to the lumber yards in Bay City and Saginaw would anchor until daylight so they could see their surroundings. Dewit Brown set up two poles in the swampy area near the mouth and hung lanterns on them at night for ships to use as navigational aids. He charged the area sawmills a small fee for his services. The United States Lighthouse Board put an end to his enterprise when they built a new lighthouse and beacon using his ingenious range light system.

Since then, several places along the Great Lakes have used range lights, including Munising and Cheboygan. It was also common to have two beacons on the long piers that reach out into the lakes to be used as range lights so that sailors could sail straight into the channel along the pier.

Chapter 24

Frozen Inside

As I scanned the horizon, I could see a massive freighter off in the distance. Thirteen ships sail on the Great Lakes that are a thousand feet in length or even a few feet longer. They are the maximum size to fit into the Soo Locks with only a few feet to spare. The bulk carrier Indiana Harbor is exactly one thousand feet long and was launched in 1979. The ship had a strange incident with the Lansing Shoal Lighthouse.

The Lansing Shoals are located in northern Lake Michigan between Squaw Island and the Upper Peninsula Shoreline. The shallow waters are a danger to ships, and a lightship was anchored at the shoal in 1901 to warn passing ships. The lighthouse board made a request for a permanent lighthouse, noting that over five thousand vessels have passed by the lightship. It was several years later that Congress authorized the funds for a lighthouse, and construction began in 1926. It was the last crib style lighthouse to be built on the Great Lakes.

Large square concrete caissons were constructed on land and then towed and sunk into position. A large slab of steel-reinforced concrete was poured over the caissons,

Lansing Shoals Lighthouse

creating a "basement" with the lighthouse constructed above. Round porthole style windows in the basement were constructed into the walls of the cribbing and allowed light to penetrate inside the structure. Half was used for living quarters and the other half for machinery to operate the light and fog signal.

The Lansing Shoal Lighthouse went into operation in 1928. The crew was taken off at the end of the shipping season in December, and an automated light remained in operation through the winter. A storm came through in early December 1929, the second year of operation, before the keepers could be removed for the season. The spray from the waves crashing against the concrete cribbing covered the lighthouse in a thick layer of ice. The crew was trapped inside for three days. Luckily, they had supplies to sustain them while they waited for the ice to melt or someone to chop away the ice in front of the door.

By 1976, the lighthouse was fully automated. The round portholes and windows in the lighthouse were bricked up, and the entire structure covered in a layer of gunite to help protect it from the elements. For the most part, the lighthouse just sat in Lake Michigan doing its thing; "out of sight and out of mind", as the saying goes. On September 3, 1993, the thousand-foot long *Indiana Harbor* struck the lighthouse. Exactly how it happened is unclear to me, but from what information I was able to gather, the autopilot was set and the crew in the pilot house was not paying attention to what was in front of them. I am sure the Lansing Shoals Lighthouse seemed tiny in relation to that massive steel freighter. A corner of the cribbing was damaged, and a fifty-foot gash was cut into the *Indiana Harbor* and cost almost two million dollars to repair. I am glad I did not have to make the call back to the owners of the ship to explain I just broke their boat because I was not looking where I was going.

Chapter 25

Ghost Light

I gathered my belongings from what's remaining of the keeper's quarters and got them ready for Captain Bob's arrival to give me a ride back to the mainland. I made the climb back up the scaffolding to get my lantern. The old lighthouse would be without a light once again unless paranormal forces somehow illuminated the lantern room like an old lighthouse on Lake Huron.

The old Presque Isle Lighthouse is one of the oldest lights still standing on the Great Lakes. It stands on an oddly shaped peninsula about fifteen miles north of Alpena. The peninsula is like an island with a small narrow strip of land that connects it to the mainland, which is where the name Presque Isle comes from. It is French for "almost island".

97

The old Presque Isle Lighthouse was constructed in 1840. The cobblestone tower is thirty feet tall and guided ships into the natural harbor for a place of refuge during the many storms that pass over Lake Huron. A taller, more powerful light was needed. About three decades after the old lighthouse was constructed, a new lighthouse was built in 1870 with a one hundred thirteen foot tall tower. It stands about a quarter mile north of the original lighthouse, and today both of them are open for tourists to visit.

In the 1990s, George Parris and his wife moved into the old keeper's cottage to run the museum and give tours. Sadly, George died at the lighthouse in 1992, and since his passing, some nights a light can be seen shining from the top of the old thirty-foot-tall tower. The beacon mysteriously comes on at dusk and goes off at dawn, which is strange since the light has been disabled and the electrical wires cut. Michigan National Guard pilots have even reported seeing the light.

After George's passing, a family with a young girl visited the lighthouse. While her family was in the museum, the girl climbed the tower. When she came back down, she told her parents she had been talking with a nice man at the top of the tower. No one else was around, so she would have been the only one in the tower. She saw a photo of Mr. Parris that hung on the wall, pointed to it, and told her parents that was the man she had been talking to.

This was not the only time people have had an encounter in the old beacon. Some visitors who climb to the top of the old tower have claimed to see a face staring back at them from inside the light fixture. George loved the lighthouse and showing visitors around the grand old structure. He was also known to play pranks on the visitors, so maybe he is playing one last prank from beyond the grave.

Sitting there waiting for my ride, I could honestly say that I have not experienced any paranormal activity either at Waugoshance Lighthouse or anywhere else. I am not sure I believe in ghosts or spirits from the beyond. I will say that the old lighthouse is creepy standing alone offshore and being circled by birds like scavengers over a dead animal.

Chapter 26

Another Birdcage

I took off my eyeglasses and pulled up the bottom of my t-shirt to wipe away the sweat from my face. I moved over into the shade created by the old lighthouse tower. I could see the shadow of the birdcage at the top of the tower. Another old lighthouse with a birdcage style lantern room still stands on the other side of Lake Michigan in Wisconsin.

The Door Peninsula protrudes out of the east side of Wisconsin into Lake Michigan to form Green Bay. It is about fifty miles long and is a popular tourist destination, but two centuries ago it was a rugged and remote coastline. In 1848, during a violent October storm, Captain Justice Bailey found a narrow safe harbor halfway up the Door Peninsula on the Lake Michigan side. After riding out the storm anchored in the small harbor, Captain Bailey explored the land to discover outcroppings of limestone and plenty of virgin timber. After completing his voyage, he sent word about his discovery to Alanson Sweet, his ship's owner.

A year later, Sweet purchased one hundred twenty-five acres of land surrounding the harbor, which was named Baileys Harbor after the captain who discovered it in an autumn storm. Sweet established a sawmill and quarry along with a pier for loading ships. Using his political connections, Sweet succeeded in having Door County created, with Baileys Harbor serving as the county seat.

In 1852, a lighthouse was constructed on an island located on the east side of the harbor. It was needed to guide ships into Baileys Harbor and Congress awarded Alanson Sweet the contract to build the new beacon. He constructed it with limestone from his quarry and topped the tower with a birdcage style lantern room that housed a sixth order Fresnel lens.

In 1866, a United States lighthouse inspector noted that the lighthouse was in "defective condition" and recommended upgrading the degrading structure. It was determined by the lighthouse board that the lighthouse location did not serve well as a guide to the harbor or a coastal light to ships sailing Lake Michigan. A new light was constructed at Cana Island, and a set of range lights were constructed to guide ships into the harbor. At the end of the sailing season in 1869, the light was permanently extinguished at the old Baileys Harbor Lighthouse.

The lighthouse and island are privately owned but still stand today. The lighthouse is in rough condition, but it was built many decades ago and left abandoned. The old weathered birdcage can still be seen from the mainland among the tops of the trees. The Cana Island Lighthouse is one of the most popular lighthouses in Wisconsin and visited by thousands of tourists every year.

Chapter 27

Wisconsin's First

A series of islands are strung along the entrance to Green Bay. Between Rock Island and St. Martin Island is the largest gap for ships to sail between. In the early days of shipping on the Great Lakes, ship owners petitioned Congress to build a lighthouse on Rock Island to guide ships through the passage into Green Bay. In 1834, Congress approved $5000 for the construction of a lighthouse on Rock Island; this was Wisconsin's first lighthouse. The lighthouse was a separate stone tower and house. The light in the tower was illuminated for the first time in October 1837. The lighthouse is known as Pottawatomie Lighthouse because of the Native Americans who had inhabited the region. The English translation of pottawatomie is "keepers of the fire", which makes it a fitting name for a lighthouse.

War of 1812 veteran David E. Corbin was appointed as the first keeper. Corbin served several years at the remote lighthouse, working alone to maintain the essential beacon. A United States Lighthouse Bureau inspector noted in 1845 that Corbin was fulfilling his duties as keeper but he was lonely with his dog and horse being his only companions. Corbin was given a leave of absence for twenty days to find a wife. It took him more than the time he was given, but he eventually married a woman with three children.

In December 1852, Corbin became ill and died. His body was laid to rest in a small cemetery on the island south of the lighthouse that he had tended for over fifteen years. In

Pottawatomie Lighthouse

104

2003, a new headstone with an image of the lighthouse carved into it was placed at his grave site.

A few decades after the first lighthouse was constructed on Rock Island, it was apparent that it was not built to withstand the harsh Wisconsin environment. In 1858, a new two-story brick lighthouse with an attached tower was constructed. The lighthouse was manned by keepers until 1946, when wet-cell batteries were installed to provide electricity to illuminate the lamp. In 1986, solar panels were installed to replace the batteries, and a few years after that, a mundane steel skeletal tower was erected near the old lighthouse to guide modern ships through the infamous passage.

The historic lighthouse was restored in 1994 to resemble what it looked like in the early 1900s. Volunteer keepers live at the lighthouse throughout the summer from Memorial Day to Labor Day, welcoming tourists and lighthouse lovers. Some of the keepers have reported strange noises during the night. They also claim that doors open and close on their own. Maybe it is the spirit of Keeper Corbin, who is still trying to fulfill his duties.

Chapter 28

Backwards in Escanaba

Each lighthouse is unique so that sailors could identify their location by looking at the beacon both at night and during the day. Some lighthouses use a similar design but may have an addition or be painted a different color to prevent it from resembling another lighthouse.

The Sand Point Lighthouse at the northern end of Ludington Park in Escanaba marks the entrance to Little Bay De Noc. It is a simple structure with a square tower, but the strange thing about this lighthouse is that the tower faces away from the water, as if it were built backwards. Nobody knows for sure why it was constructed in the orientation that it is, but I can only think it was done to distinguish it from other nearby lighthouses.

In 1867, John Terry was appointed as the first lighthouse keeper during its construction. In 1868, he became ill and died before the dwelling was completed, and his wife Mary Terry was appointed to the position of Head Lightkeeper. Because of her husband's tragic death, she was one of the first female lighthouse keepers on the Great Lakes. It was Mary who lit the Fresnel lens in the

Sand Point Lighthouse in Escanaba

tower of the lighthouse for the first time on May 13, 1868.

Mary and her late husband John did not have any children, and Mary lived alone in the lighthouse. She proudly fulfilled her duty as lightkeeper for several years until one winter night in 1886 when a fire broke out in the lighthouse, taking her life. The lighthouse was severely damaged, and no one knows what started the blaze. The rear door was forced open, and Mary's body was found on the floor in the oil-room, where fuel and supplies are stored for the lantern. Because she was found in the oil room instead of her bed, some people speculated foul play was involved.

Many people in the town of Escanaba knew Mary was careful and diligent in her duties of maintaining the lighthouse. They believed she was robbed and that the fire was set to destroy the evidence. I guess we'll never know for certain if Mary's death was an accident or intentional or why the lighthouse was seemingly built "backwards".

Chapter 29

The Keeper's Children

I was still out there looking north over Lake Michigan waiting for Captain Bob. He would have to travel past McGulpin Point Lighthouse a few miles west of Mackinaw City.

Several years ago, in the late 90s, I went over to see the lighthouse when I was visiting Mackinaw City with my wife. When I got to the driveway, it was gated off and the lighthouse was privately owned. The metal lantern room was missing, and it was only a flat base at the top of the tower. A little old lady was out working in her flower bed around the front of the lighthouse. I did not want to bother her, so I just kept on traveling down the road to Wilderness State Park.

The lighthouse was built in 1869. It is the same design that was used at Eagle Harbor and White River. For 27 years, James Davenport was the light keeper that maintained the lighthouse and sent in ice reports to the district inspector in Milwaukee.

During the end of the Great Lakes shipping season in December 1893, Keeper Davenport took a trip to Mackinaw City, Since his wife had died a few years earlier, he left his nine children in charge of the lighthouse. While he was gone, the wooden propeller driven steamer *Waldo A. Avery* burst into flames in the Straights of Mackinaw. In a desperate attempt to save the crew, the captain beached the ship at McGulpin point near the lighthouse. The lifeboats were destroyed by the fire, and the crew could not use them to get to shore in the icy waters of Lake Michigan. The keepers' resourceful children used the lighthouse skiff to rescue all 17 sailors aboard what was left of the *Waldo A. Avery*. The remains of the ship were recovered and towed to Bay City, where it was rebuilt and renamed the *Phoenix*.

In 1906, the lighthouse board decided the light was not necessary because of the Mackinac Point Lighthouse in Mackinaw City. The lighthouse was decommissioned and the lantern was removed. About ten years ago, the owner passed away, and her family either sold or donated the lighthouse to the county, which renovated the old structure and replaced the missing lantern room.

It is currently used as a museum for tourists to visit. I have climbed to the top of the tower, and the view of the Mackinac Bridge is breathtaking. I still think about the lady who lived in the lighthouse, and I regret not stopping and politely asking her if I could take a few photos of her lighthouse. In my mind, she was proud of her unique home, and I bet she would have been gracious and given me a little tour, but I guess I will never know.

Chapter 30

My Ride

Off in the distance, I could see a boat heading towards me. As it got closer, I could see that it was the *Ships Ahoy*. Captain Bob tossed a couple of rubber bumpers over the side as he floated up to the crumbling stone cribbing. He threw me some rope.

"At least you are still alive; you doing OK?"

"Yeah, I'm alright. I will feel better after I get a good meal back in town."

I grabbed my belongings and tossed them over to him with one hand while holding on to the rope with the other. Finally, I jumped down into the boat.

"It was a hell of a storm last night," I told him.

"What storm?"

"The one that came through in the middle of the night. Thunder, lightning, wind and waves; it woke me up, and I wondered if it was going to topple the old lighthouse over."

"That's odd. I slept on the boat last night, and I did not hear a thing."

With that, we pulled in the rubber bumpers and rode away from the old lighthouse. The birds circled around it, and I wondered how much longer it will be standing before Lake Michigan pulls it down.

End Notes

I wanted to clarify some things about my story and separate fact from fiction. The nonprofit group Save Waugoshance Lighthouse is a fictional organization that I used for my story. The Waugoshance Preservation Society at www.waugoshance.org is a nonprofit group that was formed to help preserve the deteriorating lighthouse. In January 2021, the organization was dissolved. They were unable to secure the funding necessary to protect the old beacon from the elements and the board decided to end the group's efforts. At this point, the Waugoshance lighthouse is truly abandoned. In the story, I also claimed that there was scaffolding in the tower. That is not true, but I needed a way in my fictional story to be able to climb to the top. It is true that the spiral staircase was stolen many years ago.

Waugoshance Lighthouse 2015

Wikipedia Creative Commons

Some facts about the Waugoshance Lighthouse

Constructed in 1850

First illuminated in 1851

Foundation: timber crib filled with stone

Tower height: 63 feet

Lens: Fourth order Fresnel

Light Distance: 16 Miles

Light Character: Fixed white varied by white flash every 45 seconds

Deactivated 1912

Resources

wwww.waugoshance.org

ww.Lighthousefriends.com

www.Seeingthelight.com (Terry Pepper)

Great Lakes Lighthouse Keepers Association
www.gllka.org

United States Lighthouse Society www.uslhs.org

Dolin, Eric Jay. *Brilliant Beacons: A History of the American Lighthouse*. Liveright Publishing Corp, 2017.

Oleszewski, Wes. *Great Lakes Lighthouses, American & Canadian: A Comprehensive Directory/Guide to Great Lakes Lighthouses*. Avery Color Studios, 1998.

Stonehouse, Frederick. *Haunted Lakes: Great Lakes Ghost Stories, Superstitions, and Sea Serpents*. Lake Superior Port Cities, 1997.

Kotzian, John. *Sky Pilot of the Great Lakes: A Biography of the Reverend William H. Law*. Avery Color Studios, Inc., 2014.

Kozma, LuAnne Gaykowski. *Living at a Lighthouse: Oral Histories from the Great Lakes*. Great Lakes Lighthouse Keepers Association, 1987.

Stonehouse, Frederick. *Lighthouse Tales Great Lakes*. Avery Color Studios, 1998.

Hoyt, Susan Roark. *Lighthouses of Southwest Michigan*. Arcadia Publishing, 2003

Stonehouse, Frederick. *Haunted Lakes II: More Great Lakes Ghost Stories*. Lake Superior Port Cities, 2000.

The images in the book were converted in photoshop using a pencil sketch filter. Sources of the images are listed below.

Inside title page. Wikipedia Creative Commons

Page 21. Coast Guard Archives

Page 24. Wikipedia Creative Commons

Page 41. Wikipedia Creative Commons

Page 45. U.S. Navy archives

Page 51. Author's Photo

Page 60. Wikepidia Creative Commons

Page 75. Coast Guard Archives

Page 80. Author's Photo

Page 85. Wikipedia Creative Commons

Page 94. Author's Photo

Page 104. Coast Guard Archives

Page 107. Author's Photo

About The Author

Mike Sonnenberg was born and raised in Saginaw Michigan where he currently resides. He worked in the automotive industry designing test and assembly machines for about 20 years. Starting in 2013 he began traveling the back roads of Michigan in search of forgotten or overlooked places. He created the Lost In Michigan website posting photos and stories of the interesting places he has found. Sonnenberg's work has been featured in the Detroit Free Press and he is considered a "Michigan Expert" by USA Today. In the fall of 2017, he published his first of five books based on the posts on his website. He still continues to travel around Michigan looking for unique places to tell their story. You can follow his journey at www.LostinMichigan.net

Made in the USA
Monee, IL
30 November 2021

fcd539a5-e995-4f20-be12-e67086eb2e32R01